It's another Quality Book from CGP

This book has been carefully written for Year 4 children learning science. It's full of questions and investigations designed to cover the Year 4 objectives on 'Sound' from the latest National Curriculum.

There's also plenty of practice at 'Working Scientifically' throughout the book.

What CGP is all about

Our sole aim here at CGP is to produce the highest quality books — carefully written, immaculately presented and dangerously close to being funny.

Then we work our socks off to get them out to you — at the cheapest possible prices.

Name: .... Class: ....

KS2 Science
Year 4 Workout

CGP
- books like no others!

CGP

Sound

More brilliant books for Year 4 Science...

...have you got yours?

Contents

Answers to the questions are on the back of the Pull-out Poster in the centre of the book.

Published by CGP

Contributors
Katie Braid, Sean Stayte
With thanks to Rachel Kordan and Maxine Petrie for the proofreading.

ISBN: 978 1 78294 086 9

Clipart from Corel®
Printed by Elanders Ltd, Newcastle upon Tyne.
Based on the classic CGP style created by Richard Parsons.

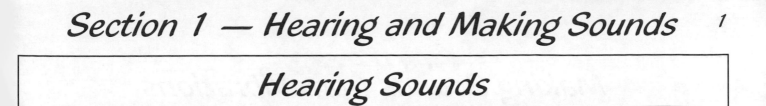

Hearing Sounds

We hear sounds with our ears. Sounds can tell you <u>what</u> something is, and <u>where</u> it is.
That's how an owl can tell where a mouse is when it hears a squeak.

1. For each thing below, write the sound it makes in the bubble.
Then write below it whether the sound is '**loud**' or '**quiet**'.

...tick tock...

......quiet......

2. The girl below can **hear** a police siren. The pictures show **three** places the car **could** be.
For each one, read what she's thinking then (circle) the right position of the car.

The siren is very quiet, but it's getting louder.

Now the siren is getting quieter.

3. Mr. Fisher's cat and dog are watching TV.
Why do they point their **ears** towards the door when he comes in?

....

....

....

One Man And His Dog

<u>**INVESTIGATE**</u> ....
Make a list of all the sounds you can hear right now. Say what the sound is like, what
made it, and whether it is loud or quiet. Are any of the sounds getting louder or quieter?

Making Sounds from Vibrations

All sounds are made in the <u>same way</u> — by things <u>vibrating</u>.
(That means moving to and fro really quickly.)

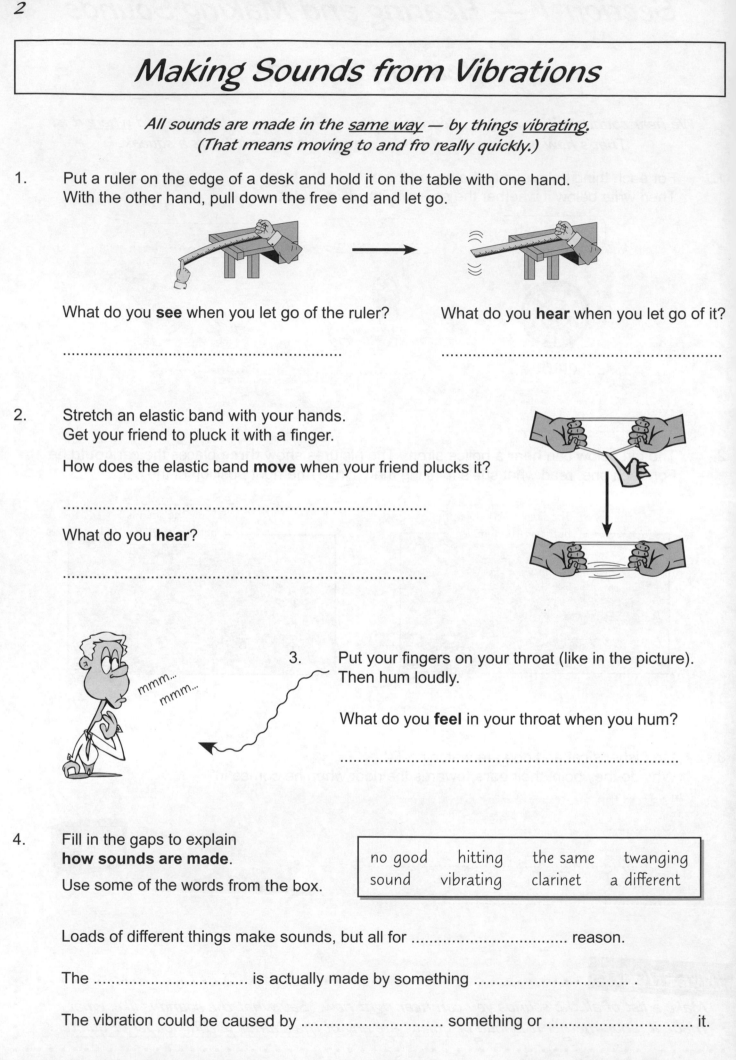

1. Put a ruler on the edge of a desk and hold it on the table with one hand.
    With the other hand, pull down the free end and let go.

    What do you **see** when you let go of the ruler?

    ....

    What do you **hear** when you let go of it?

    ....

2. Stretch an elastic band with your hands.
    Get your friend to pluck it with a finger.

    How does the elastic band **move** when your friend plucks it?

    ....

    What do you **hear**?

    ....

    mmm... mmm...

3. Put your fingers on your throat (like in the picture).
    Then hum loudly.

    What do you **feel** in your throat when you hum?

    ....

4. Fill in the gaps to explain
    how sounds are made.

    Use some of the words from the box.

no good	hitting	the same	twanging
sound	vibrating	clarinet	a different

    Loads of different things make sounds, but all for .... reason.

    The .... is actually made by something ....

    The vibration could be caused by .... something or .... it.

Making Sounds from Vibrations

5.   The pictures show a **tuning fork** being struck.

When you hit a tuning fork against a
solid object, it makes a ringing sound...

... and if you put it in water while it's still
ringing, the water sprays everywhere.

Circle the right words in **bold** to make the sentences correct.

> When you hit a tuning fork against a table, it makes a **wailing / ringing** sound.
>
> That's because the prongs **vibrate / stay still**.
>
> You can tell that **the prongs are / your hand is** vibrating because when you put
>
> the tuning fork straight into water, it **freezes / sprays everywhere**.

*Never touch glass with a
vibrating tuning fork. If you
did, it would shatter the glass.*

6.   Gertrude has just hit this **cymbal**.

What is the cymbal **doing** that
causes it to make a noise?

....

What will she **feel** if she grabs hold of the edge of the cymbal?

....

7.   Helga has a drum with rice on it. Why does the rice
fly up in the air when she **hits** the drum?

....

....

INVESTIGATE •

- *Draw a table with two columns. In the first, make a list of any musical instruments you*
- *can think of. In the second, see if you can name the bit of the instrument that vibrates.*
- *As an extra challenge, draw diagrams to explain how each instrument makes a sound.*

Sound Travels Through Things

The vibrations from a sound can <u>travel</u> to our ears through loads of <u>different things</u>.
They travel really easily through air, but they also travel through <u>other things</u>, like walls.

1. In each picture, sound is travelling from the clock to the man's ear.
    Write underneath each one **what** the vibrations are **travelling through**.

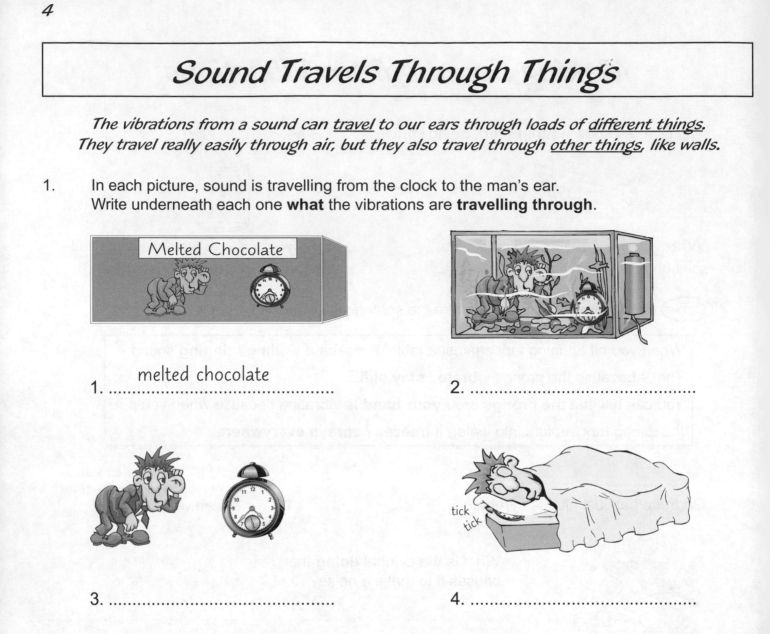

1. melted chocolate ....

2. ....

3. ....

4. ....

2. Anya is making a noise. There are two people and a fish who can **hear** it. Pick out the things
    from the list below that the vibrations have gone **through** to get to each one.

    water   cloth   glass   air   metal

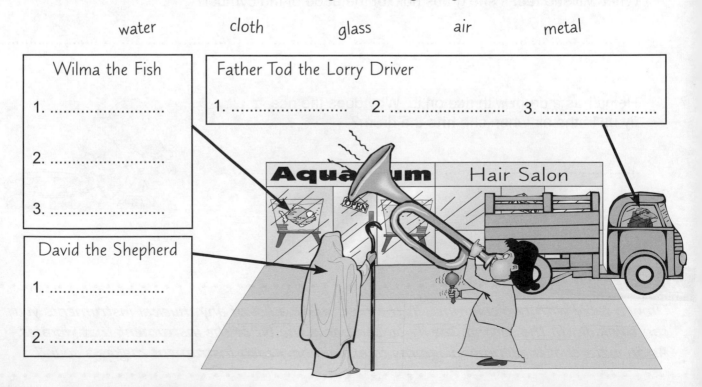

Wilma the Fish

1. ....

2. ....

3. ....

David the Shepherd

1. ....

2. ....

Father Tod the Lorry Driver

1. ....   2. ....   3. ....

Sound Travels Through Things

3. Which **three** materials do the vibrations from Chris's stereo **travel through** before they get to the dolphin?

....
....
....

Which **four** materials do the vibrations from Chris's stereo **travel through** to get to the people in the submarine?

....
....
....
....

4. Which **materials** do the vibrations from the bird's loudspeaker **travel through** to reach the girl's ears?

The vibrations travel through:

1) .... air ....

2) ....

3) ....

4) ....

5) ....

INVESTIGATE

• Write down all the different sounds you can hear right now. For each one, try to write down all the different things the sound has travelled through to reach your ears.
• Is there a link between how loud a sound is and how many things it has gone through?

Volume

The volume of a sound means how <u>quiet</u> or how <u>loud</u> it is. The volume of a sound depends on how <u>strong</u> the vibrations making it are and how <u>far away</u> from it you are.

1.   Bertie is hitting a drum, but wants to make it sound **louder**.
      Tick (✔) the best way for him to do this.

      Hit it harder ☐   Use a softer stick ☐

                  Paint the drum a different colour ☐

      Hit it more often ☐   Shout at the drum ☐

2.   (Circle) the right words to finish off this paragraph about **loudness**.

      If you want to make a drum sound louder, you have to hit it **harder / softer** .

      If you want to make a stringed instrument sound louder, you have to **bite / pluck** the

      strings **harder / more softly** . Some string instruments are played by dragging a

      cat / bow across the strings to make them **vibrate / shorter** . To make a violin sound

      quieter you have to drag the bow **harder / more softly** across the strings.

3.   Use the words below to **complete** these sentences about how **bells** ring.

      When you shake a bell, the .... or .... inside knocks

      against the outside. The noise is made by the .... bit on the outside which

      .... when the hammer or ball hits it. The .... you shake

      the bell, the more it vibrates and the .... it rings.

Volume

4. Put a tick (✔) next to all the sentences that are correct.

A	If something is loud but far away it will sound quiet.	☐

D	Sounds get quieter as you move away from the source.	☐

B	The stronger the vibrations are the louder the noise is.	☐

E	If something loud is really far away it sounds even louder.	☐

C	Weak vibrations cause loud noises.	☐

F	Sounds get louder as you move away from the source.	☐

5. Hillary, Barbara and George all went to a rock concert. Afterwards, they told each other whether they enjoyed it. Write names under each sentence to show who said what.

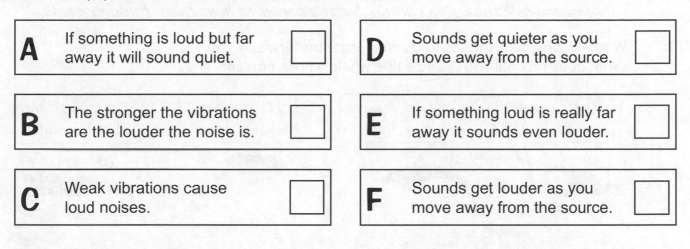

Hillary   Barbara   George

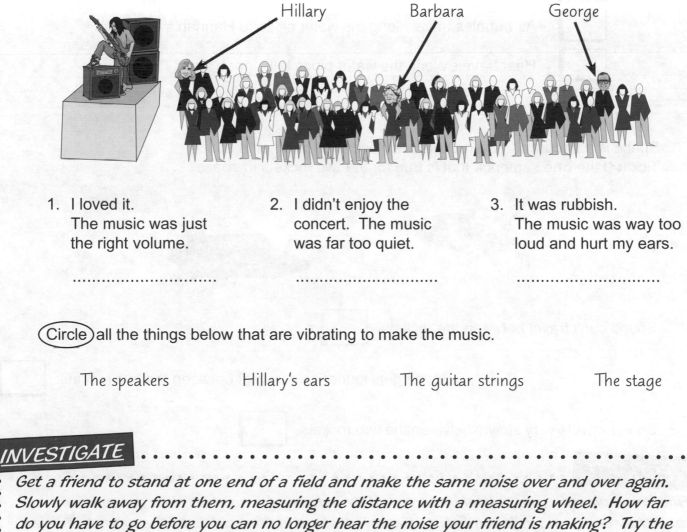

1. I loved it.
   The music was just
   the right volume.

   ....

2. I didn't enjoy the
   concert. The music
   was far too quiet.

   ....

3. It was rubbish.
   The music was way too
   loud and hurt my ears.

   ....

Circle all the things below that are vibrating to make the music.

The speakers   Hillary's ears   The guitar strings   The stage

INVESTIGATE ....

• Get a friend to stand at one end of a field and make the same noise over and over again.
• Slowly walk away from them, measuring the distance with a measuring wheel. How far
• do you have to go before you can no longer hear the noise your friend is making? Try the
• same thing with a louder noise and a quieter noise. What do you notice?

Section 2 — Volume of Sounds

8

Sound Travelling

Sound travels much __better__ through __some materials__ than others. For example, you can hear someone talk through a curtain, but it's harder to hear them through a wall.

1. Whales can make sounds to communicate **underwater**.
    What does that tell you? (Circle) the whale who is **correct**.

Water makes sounds quieter. — John

Water makes sounds louder. — Tony

Water makes whales clever. — Gordon

Sound can travel through water. — Margaret

2. Hannah and Colin are in different rooms. The rooms have radiators that are **connected** by water pipes. Hannah puts her **ear** to the radiator in her room. Tick (✔) the box that explains why she can **hear** Colin tapping on his radiator.

    ☐ The vibrations travel along the water pipes to Hannah's ear.

    ☐ Air bubbles travel along the water pipes to Hannah's ear.

    ☐ Heat travels along the water pipes to Hannah's ear.

3. Space is a **vacuum**. Two rockets are close to each other in space.
    Tick (✔) the **one** sentence that is true for the two rockets in space.

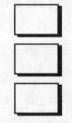

Sound can't travel between the rockets. ☐

Sound gets louder as it travels between the two rockets. ☐

Sound travels very slowly between the two rockets. ☐

INVESTIGATE

Find some pipes in your school or home. Make sure they're not hot, then get someone to tap gently on them while you listen. First of all stand in the middle of the room and listen, then move closer to a part of the pipe and listen. Can you hear the tapping?

Stopping Sound from Travelling

Although you often want to hear sounds, sometimes you want to <u>stop</u> a sound completely. I like to listen to music, but I have to <u>muffle</u> the sound of my little brother yelling.

1. Use the **words** from the box to **complete** these sentences.

    | louder | more muffled | damage | loud | quiet | decorate |

    Sometimes it's useful to stop sound travelling, because really .... noises

    can .... your ears. Fairly loud noises like footsteps in a school corridor

    can disturb people, so it's better if the corridor makes the sound ....

2.   Match each reason for stopping sound travelling with a way to
    stop it — join them up by drawing a **line** between them.

    So you don't damage your ears.   Thick walls

    So sound doesn't disturb neighbours.   Thick fluffy carpet

    So footsteps don't disturb people.   Ear protectors

    Write down a way to stop sound travelling through windows.

    ....

3. Hilda is hiking in her new steel boots.
    Put a tick (✔) next to the places where her footsteps would sound very **loud**.

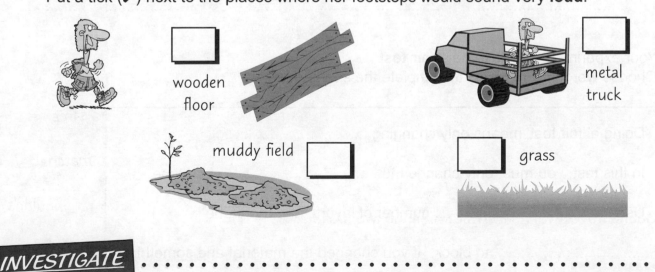

wooden floor

metal truck

muddy field

grass

INVESTIGATE ....

*   *Make a list of the floor coverings in your house or school (e.g. kitchen tiles, carpet, etc.).*
*   *Write down which ones make a loud noise when you walk on them, and which ones muffle*
*   *the sound. Does it make a difference what you're wearing on your feet?*

Section 2 — Volume of Sounds

MINI-PROJECT

Muffling Sound

Muffling material

Noise

Your challenge for this mini-project is to find the <u>best material</u> to stuff into a pair of earmuffs to <u>block out noise</u>. Work through each question to do your experiment correctly.

1. Here are the materials you could use to block out noise.

Put a tick (✔) next to those you think will be good, and a cross (✘) next to those you think will be bad. Explain your answer for each one.

☐ Newspaper ....

☐ Bubble wrap ....

☐ Cotton wool ....

☐ Wool ....

☐ Cotton sheet ....

☐ Netting ....

Now choose **3** materials to test (either from the list or your own choice):

1. .... 2. .... 3. ....

2. Your experiment needs to be a **fair test**.
Choose words from the list to complete the sentences.

Doing a 'fair test' means only changing ....

In this test, you must only change the .... each time.

Use the .... number of layers, and the same

.... to block. If you changed the material and something

else as well, you .... know what caused the result.

same

material

wouldn't

sound

one thing

Muffling Sound

MINI-PROJECT

3. **Test the three materials** you chose in part 1 by wrapping them around something that is making a noise, and seeing how much of the noise they block.

Write down **what** you are using that makes a **noise**: ....

Write down **how many layers** of each material you'll use: ....

Test each material in turn, then write your results in this table:

Material	How good it was at blocking out the noise.

4. Use your results and the sentence below to explain which are the **best and worst materials** for the earmuffs.

> Materials that muffle sounds don't let vibrations travel through them easily.

The **best** material to use is ....

because ....

The **worst** material to use is ....

because ....

If you tested any of the materials from the list in Q1, do your results match what you expected?

....

EXTRA PROJECT

Make an advert for your earmuffs, explaining the science behind your choice of material. You could draw a magazine or web ad, or even write a TV script.

Section 3 — Pitch

Pitch Means How High

*A sound can be <u>high pitched</u> or <u>low pitched</u>. A bird cheeping is
high pitched and my stomach rumbling is low pitched.*

1. Use **some** of the words in the oval to fill in the gaps.

    The pitch of a note is how high or how .... it is.

    A whistle makes a .... pitched sound.

    A bass-drum makes a .... pitched sound.

    A good example of a high pitched sound is a ....

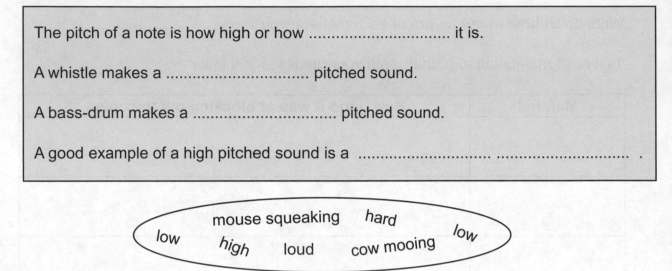

mouse squeaking   hard
low   high   loud   cow mooing   low

2. For each of these instruments, write **high pitch** or **low pitch** underneath its name.

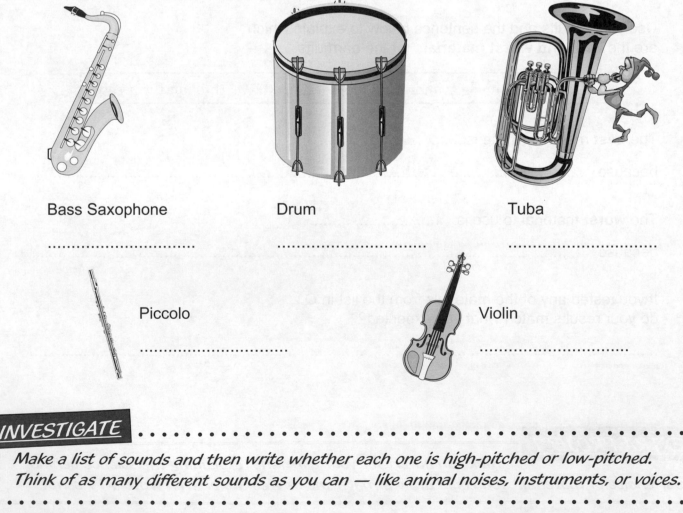

Bass Saxophone

....

Drum

....

Tuba

....

Piccolo

....

Violin

....

INVESTIGATE . . . .

·   *Make a list of sounds and then write whether each one is high-pitched or low-pitched.*
·   *Think of as many different sounds as you can — like animal noises, instruments, or voices.*

Answers to Y4 'Sound'

Section 3 — Pitch

Page 12 — Pitch Means How High

1. low, high, low, mouse squeaking
2. Bass Saxophone — Low
   Drum — Low
   Tuba — Low
   Piccolo — High
   Violin — High

Page 13 — Pitch and Volume

1. 1. high, quiet   2. low, quiet
   3. high, loud   4. low, loud
2. high, low, loud, quiet, nothing
3. E.g. Uncle Egbert is wrong because pitch and volume are different. High sounds can be loud and low sounds can be quiet.

Pages 14-15 — The Pitch of a Drum

1. Drum 1: very high   Drum 2: fairly high
   Drum 3: fairly low   Drum 4: very low
2. From lowest to highest: 5, 1, 2, 3, 4
3. tighter
   It'll get higher.
4. A — high
   B — high
   C — low
   D — medium
   E — medium

Pages 16-17 — Making an Instrument

1. The following sentences should be circled: How much the elastic band is being stretched. The length of the elastic band.
2. cereal box, four elastic bands, scissors
3. Depends on your elastic bands.
4. Depends on your results. Band A should have the highest pitch and Band D the lowest.
5. Either: thicker, lower, pitch.
   Or: thinner, higher, pitch.
6. The new band will have a higher pitch than Band A.
7. The new band will have a lower pitch than Band D.

Pages 18-19 — The Pitch of Stringed Instruments

1. From highest to lowest: violin, viola, cello, double bass
2. From highest to lowest: C, A, B
3. 1. The thin string should be ticked.
   2. The short string should be ticked.
   3. The tight string should be ticked.
4. skin, string, thinner, shorter, tightening
5.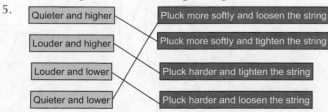

Pages 20-21 — The Pitch of Wind Instruments

1. vibrating, strings, drum, air
2. These words should be circled: higher, higher
3. All the smaller instruments are higher.
   The trumpet with a loop is lower than the one without.

4&5.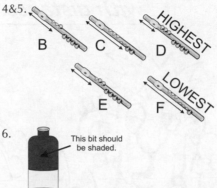

6.
   This bit should be shaded.

   These should be ticked: tip some water out of the bottle, put some more water in the bottle.

Mixed Questions — Pages 22-25

1. Aeroplane — loud   Mouse — quiet
   Racing Car — loud   Thunderstorm — loud
2. Hit it harder.
3. They vibrate.
4. Drum — the skin vibrates
   Guitar — the strings vibrate
   Trumpet — the air inside vibrates
   Violin — the strings vibrate
5. These materials should be circled: a duvet, cotton wool, a big woolly jumper.
6. lower, higher, air, shorter
7. air, metal, water
   The shark's ears.
8. Field C
9. A, C, higher
10. Drums C and D should be ticked.
    Drum C has a higher pitch because the skin is tighter.
    Drum D has a higher pitch because it is smaller.
    Drums B and E should be ticked.
    Drum B has a lower pitch because it is bigger.
    Drum E has a lower pitch because the skin is looser.
11. The sound would be louder because the air in the bottle would be vibrating more.
    The sound would be quieter because the air in the bottle would be vibrating less.
    The sound would have a higher pitch because the vibrating column of air would be smaller.
    The sound would have a lower pitch because the vibrating column of air would be larger.
12. E.g. because the sound travels along the pipe to Bernard's ears / because the vibrations travel better through the pipe than through the air.

Answers to Y4 'Sound'

Section 1 — Hearing and Making Sounds

Page 1 — Hearing Sounds

1. Snake: e.g. hiss, quiet
    Lion: e.g roar, loud

2.

3. Because they hear a sound and point their ears to the door to hear better.

Pages 2-3 — Making Sounds from Vibrations

1. The ruler moves up and down until it slows down and stops.
    You can hear a twanging noise.

2. The elastic band wobbles back and forth until it slows down and stops.
    You can hear a twanging noise.

3. You can feel a vibration or slight tickly feeling.

4. the same, sound, vibrating, hitting, twanging

5. ringing, vibrate, the prongs are, sprays everywhere

6. The cymbal vibrates to make a noise.
    She will feel the cymbal vibrating.

7. Because the skin of the drum is vibrating.

Pages 4-5 — Sound Travels Through Things

1. 2. water
    3. air
    4. pillow

2. Wilma
    1. air 2. glass 3. water
    David:
    1. air 2. cloth
    Father Tod:
    1. air 2. glass 3. metal

3. To get to the dolphin: rubber, air, water.
    To get to the submarine: rubber, air, water, metal.

4. air, glass, wood, bricks, plaster

Section 2 — Volume of Sounds

Pages 6-7 — Volume

1. Hit it harder.

2. The following words should be circled: harder, pluck, harder, bow, vibrate, more softly.

3. ball, hammer, metal, vibrates, harder, louder

4. These sentences should be ticked: A, B, D.

5. 1. Barbara 2. George 3. Hillary
    The speakers, the guitar strings.

Page 8 — Sound Travelling

1. Margaret should be circled.

2. The vibrations travel along the water pipes to Hannah's ear.

3. Sound can't travel between the rockets.

Page 9 — Stopping Sound from Travelling

1. loud, damage, more muffled

2.
So you don't damage your ears.	Thick walls
So sound doesn't disturb neighbours.	Thick fluffy carpet
So footsteps don't disturb people.	Ear protectors

    E.g. double glazing, thick curtains

3. These boxes should be ticked: wooden floor, metal truck.

Pages 10-11 — Muffling Sound

1. For example:
    ✘ Newspaper — because it is very thin.
    ✔ Bubble wrap — because it has loads of layers of plastic.
    ✔ Cotton wool — because it is thick and padded.
    ✔ Wool — because it is thick and padded.
    ✘ Cotton sheet — because it is very thin.
    ✘ Netting— because it has lots of holes in it.

2. one thing, material, same, sound, wouldn't

3. Any sensible answer is OK. For example, you could use a buzzer to make a noise.

4. Depends on your results. Any sensible answer is OK.

Pitch and Volume

Pitch is <u>totally different</u> to volume. It's easy to get them mixed up,
but just remember — things can be loud or quiet, <u>and</u> high or low.

1.   Look at the pictures below and decide whether the sounds being made are
loud or **quiet**, **high** or **low**. (Circle) the right words to finish the sentences.

1. The chick is making a
high / **low** sound.
The sound is **loud** / **quiet**.

2. Akiro's belly is making
a **high** / **low** sound.
The sound is **loud** / **quiet**.

3. Maria is making
a **high** / **low** sound.
The sound is **loud** / **quiet**.

4. Wayne's truck is making
a **high** / **low** sound.
The sound is **loud** / **quiet**.

2.   Using the words in the boxes, fill in the blanks to complete this paragraph
about **pitch** and **loudness**. You won't need to use all the words.

Pitch describes how .... or

.... a sound is. Both low and high sounds can be

either .... or ....

Pitch has .... to do with loudness.

Boxes: HIGH, LOUD, NOTHING, QUIET, LOW, EVERYTHING

3.   My Uncle Egbert reckons all high sounds are **quiet** and all low sounds are **loud**.
Is he right? Explain your answer.

Uncle Egbert is .... because ....

....

INVESTIGATE ·
Whistle (or sing) a high-pitched note (not too loudly please). Then see if you can make the
same note as quietly as possible. Try to do the same thing with a low-pitched note.

Section 3 — Pitch

The Pitch of a Drum

*Drums come in all different shapes and sizes. A drum's pitch depends on its size and
how tight the skin is. The bigger the drum and looser the skin, the lower the pitch.*

1. Douglas tried playing **four** drums. Some of them made high-pitched sounds and some made
    low-pitched sounds. Use words in the box to **describe the pitch** of each drum.

very low	fairly low	fairly high	very high

*You should
only use each
description once.*

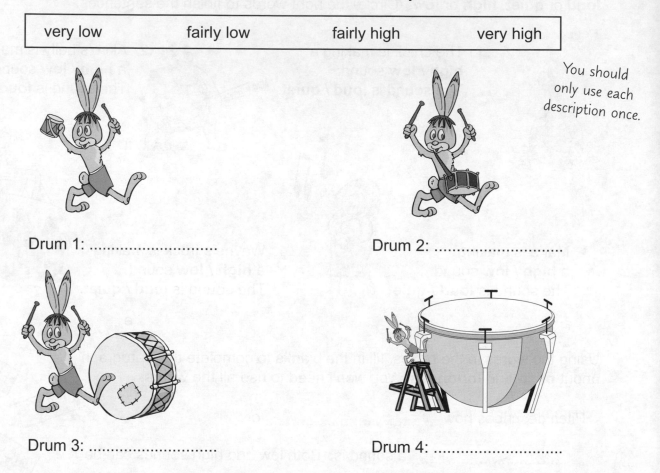

Drum 1: ....

Drum 2: ....

Drum 3: ....

Drum 4: ....

2. Here are some more drums. Which one will be the **highest**? Which one will be the **lowest**?
    Write down the **numbers** of the drums, putting them in **order** of how high pitched they are.

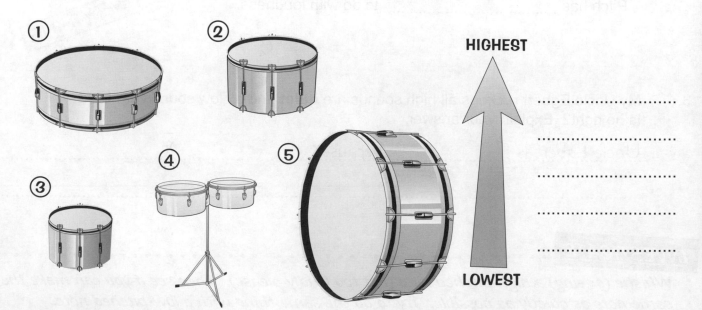

HIGHEST

....

....

....

....

....

LOWEST

The Pitch of a Drum

3.   If the screws on this drum are **turned** so that the skin is **pulled** downwards at the edges, will the skin get **tighter** or **slacker**?

....

What will happen to the **sound** the drum makes?
Tick (✔) the box next to the right answer.

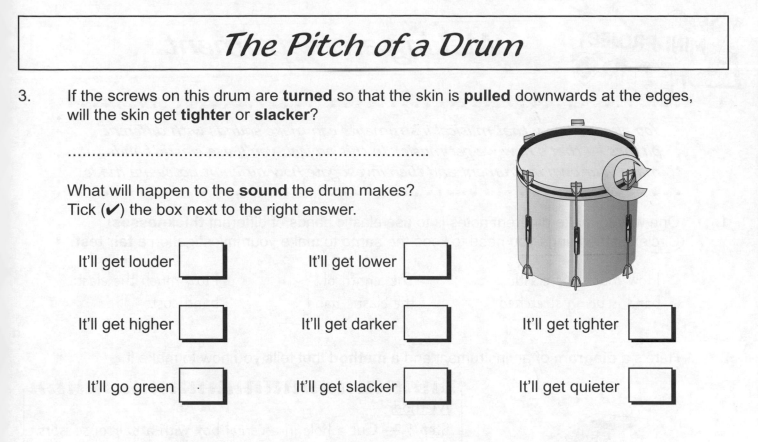

It'll get louder ☐   It'll get lower ☐

It'll get higher ☐   It'll get darker ☐   It'll get tighter ☐

It'll go green ☐   It'll get slacker ☐   It'll get quieter ☐

4.   This drum kit has several different drums. Read how **tight** each drum is, and then decide whether its pitch is **high**, **medium** or **low**. Write your answer in the label for each drum.

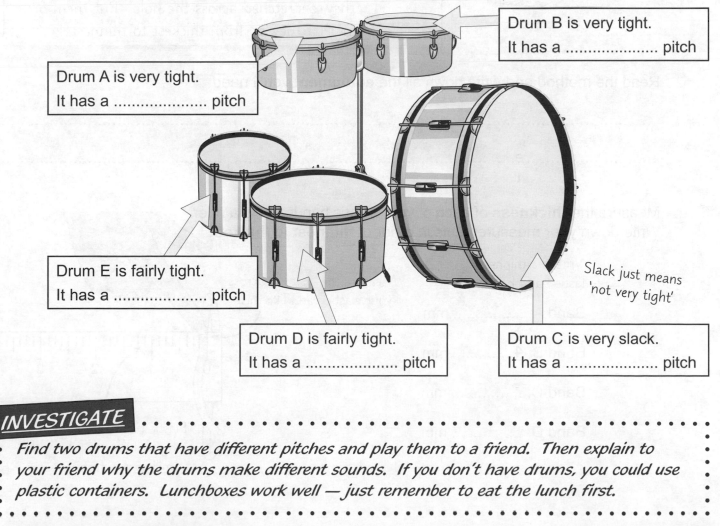

Drum B is very tight.
It has a .... pitch

Drum A is very tight.
It has a .... pitch

Drum E is fairly tight.
It has a .... pitch

Drum D is fairly tight.
It has a .... pitch

Drum C is very slack.
It has a .... pitch

Slack just means 'not very tight'

INVESTIGATE ....

· *Find two drums that have different pitches and play them to a friend. Then explain to*
· *your friend why the drums make different sounds. If you don't have drums, you could use*
· *plastic containers. Lunchboxes work well — just remember to eat the lunch first.*

MINI-PROJECT

Making an Instrument

You already know that musical instruments can make sounds with different pitches — that's how we get music. In this project, you'll use elastic bands to make your own instrument and then investigate how different notes are made.

1. One way to make different notes is to use elastic bands of different **thicknesses**. Circle all the things you need to keep the **same** to make your investigation a **fair test**.

| How much the elastic band is being stretched. | The length of the elastic band. | How much the elastic band cost. |

2. Here's a **diagram** of an instrument and a **method** that tells you how to make it.

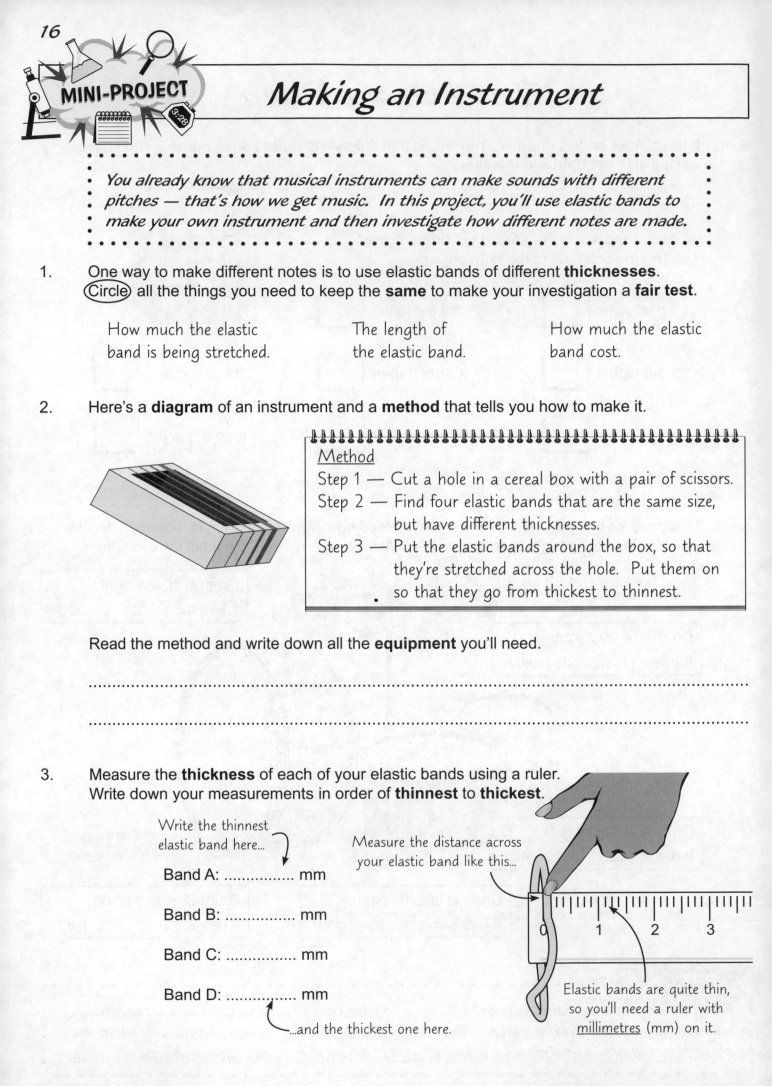

Method
Step 1 — Cut a hole in a cereal box with a pair of scissors.
Step 2 — Find four elastic bands that are the same size, but have different thicknesses.
Step 3 — Put the elastic bands around the box, so that they're stretched across the hole. Put them on so that they go from thickest to thinnest.

Read the method and write down all the **equipment** you'll need.

....

....

3. Measure the **thickness** of each of your elastic bands using a ruler. Write down your measurements in order of **thinnest** to **thickest**.

Write the thinnest elastic band here...

Band A: .... mm

Band B: .... mm

Band C: .... mm

Band D: .... mm

...and the thickest one here.

Measure the distance across your elastic band like this...

Elastic bands are quite thin, so you'll need a ruler with millimetres (mm) on it.

Making an Instrument

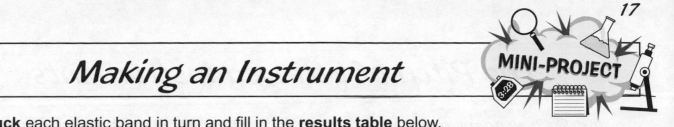

4. **Pluck** each elastic band in turn and fill in the **results table** below.

Band	Thickness (in mm)	Pitch
A		
B		
C		
D		

Use words like <u>very low</u> or <u>fairly high</u> to fill in the Pitch column.

5. Circle **one** word from each elastic band to write a **conclusion** for your experiment.

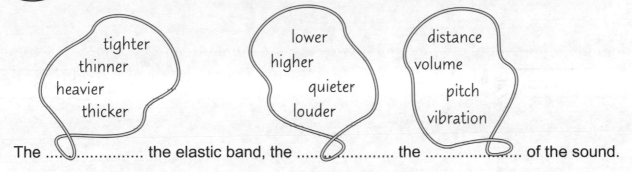

tighter
thinner
heavier
thicker

lower
higher
quieter
louder

distance
volume
pitch
vibration

The .... the elastic band, the .... the .... of the sound.

6. If you added a **thinner** elastic band to your instrument, what do you think would happen? Put a tick (✔) next to your answer.

The new band will have a higher pitch than Band A.

The new band will have a lower pitch than Band A.

7. If you added a **thicker** elastic band to your instrument, what do you think would happen? Put a tick (✔) next to your answer.

The new band will have a higher pitch than Band D.

The new band will have a lower pitch than Band D.

EXTRA PROJECT

You've found out that the sound the instrument makes depends on how thick the elastic bands are. Now make a list of all the other things that you think might affect the sound. Then pick one, make a plan and carry out an investigation into it.

The Pitch of Stringed Instruments

Just like how drums sound <u>higher</u> if the skin is <u>smaller</u> or <u>tighter</u>, <u>stringed instruments</u> sound <u>higher</u> if the string is <u>shorter</u> or <u>tighter</u> — and also if the string is <u>thinner</u>.

1.   Take a look at these different **stringed instruments**, and write them in order of **pitch**, with the highest pitch first.

HINT: Look at the length of the string in each picture.

cello

viola

double bass

violin

....

| Highest Pitch | | Lowest Pitch |

2.   Jimbo is playing some heavy metal on his new guitar. Write the letters from each picture in order of **pitch**, with the **highest** pitch first.

HINT: Look at where his hands are and think about which part of the string is vibrating.

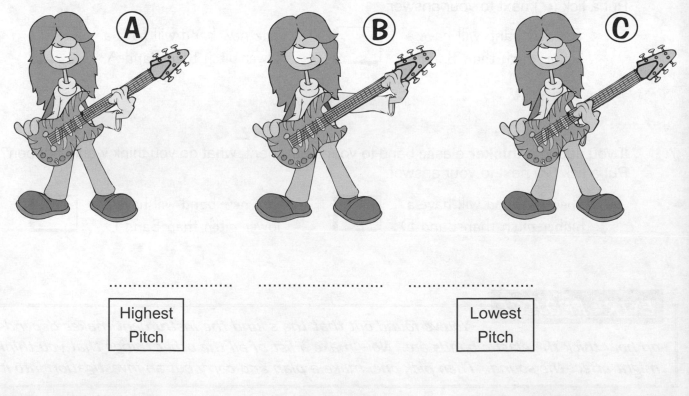

....

| Highest Pitch | | Lowest Pitch |

The Pitch of Stringed Instruments

3. For each **pair** of strings, put a tick (✔) next to the one that would have the **highest** pitch.

1.

2.

3.

tight *loose*

4. Fill in the **gaps** using the words on the cello.

tightening *shorter* *thinner* *skin* *string*

To make the pitch of a drum higher, you could make the .... tighter. The pitch of a stringed instrument can be changed by using a different type of ....

As well as making the string .... or ...., you could make the pitch higher by .... the string using the tuning pegs.

5. Draw a **line** from each light box to a dark box to show how you would change the sound of a **guitar string**. The first one has been done for you.

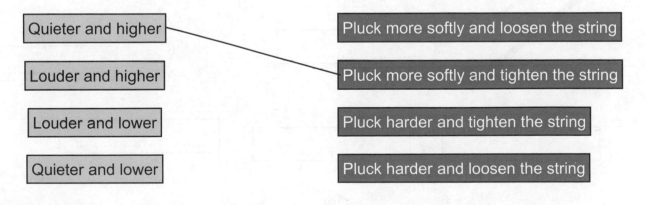

Quieter and higher — Pluck more softly and tighten the string

Louder and higher — Pluck more softly and loosen the string

Louder and lower — Pluck harder and tighten the string

Quieter and lower — Pluck harder and loosen the string

INVESTIGATE

· Draw a poster with a design for one string instrument that will be low pitched and one string instrument that will be high pitched. Label all the different parts of the instruments and explain why they make sounds of different pitches. Include as much detail as you can.

Section 3 — Pitch

The Pitch of Wind Instruments

OK, this is how it works — the <u>more</u> air that is vibrating, the <u>lower</u> the pitch.
So, the <u>longer</u> the pipe of a wind instrument is, the <u>lower</u> it will sound.

1. Use **some** of the words in the box below to fill in the gaps in the sentences.

air	guitar	vibrating	drum	strings	skin

    Sound is caused by something .... A guitar makes sound when the plucked

    .... vibrate. When you beat a .... the skin vibrates to make the

    noise. In a wind instrument like a flute, it's the .... inside that vibrates.

2. Circle **one** word from each pair in brackets to complete these sentences.

    With string instruments the **shorter** the string, the (**higher** / **lower**) the pitch.

    With wind instruments the **less** air there is to vibrate, the (**higher** / **lower**) the pitch.

3. Each of these pictures shows two different sizes of the same kind of instrument.
    For each pair write **higher** or **lower** next to the right instrument to describe their **pitch**.

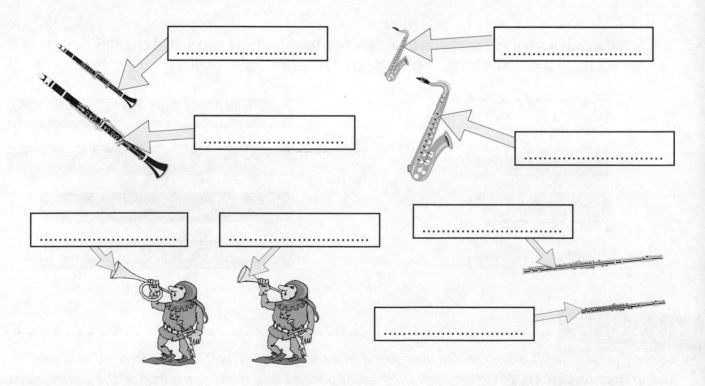

The Pitch of Wind Instruments

4. Here are some pictures of flutes with **open** and **closed** keys. Draw an **arrow** next to each one to show how long the column of vibrating air is. The first one has been done for you.

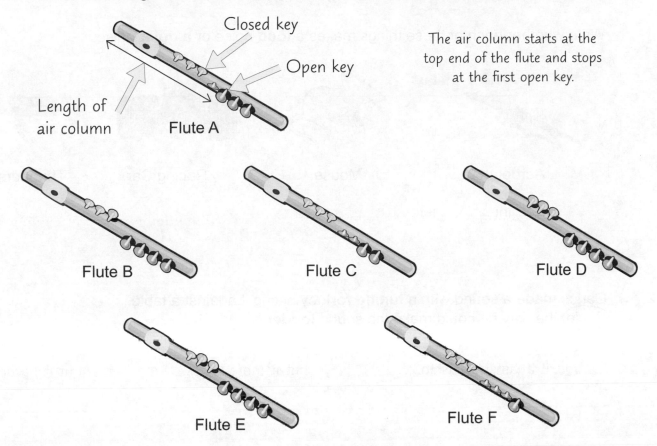

Closed key

Open key

The air column starts at the top end of the flute and stops at the first open key.

Length of air column

Flute A

Flute B

Flute C

Flute D

Flute E

Flute F

5. Have another look at the flutes and write **highest** next to the flute which will make the highest pitched sound and **lowest** next to the flute which will make the lowest pitched sound.

6. Greg is making a sound by **blowing** over the top of a bottle filled with water. Look at the picture and **shade in** the air that is vibrating.

Put a tick (✔) next to all the ways that Greg could change the **pitch** of his sound.

☐ Blow harder over the top.

☐ Tip some water out of the bottle.

☐ Put some more water in the bottle.

INVESTIGATE

Fill some empty bottles with different amounts of water. Put them in order from what you think will be the highest pitch to lowest pitch. Then test them to see if you got it right.

Mixed Questions

Here's a load of questions all about sound. They cover all the topics in this book, specially written, just for you.

1. Write whether each of these things makes a **loud** noise or a **quiet** noise.

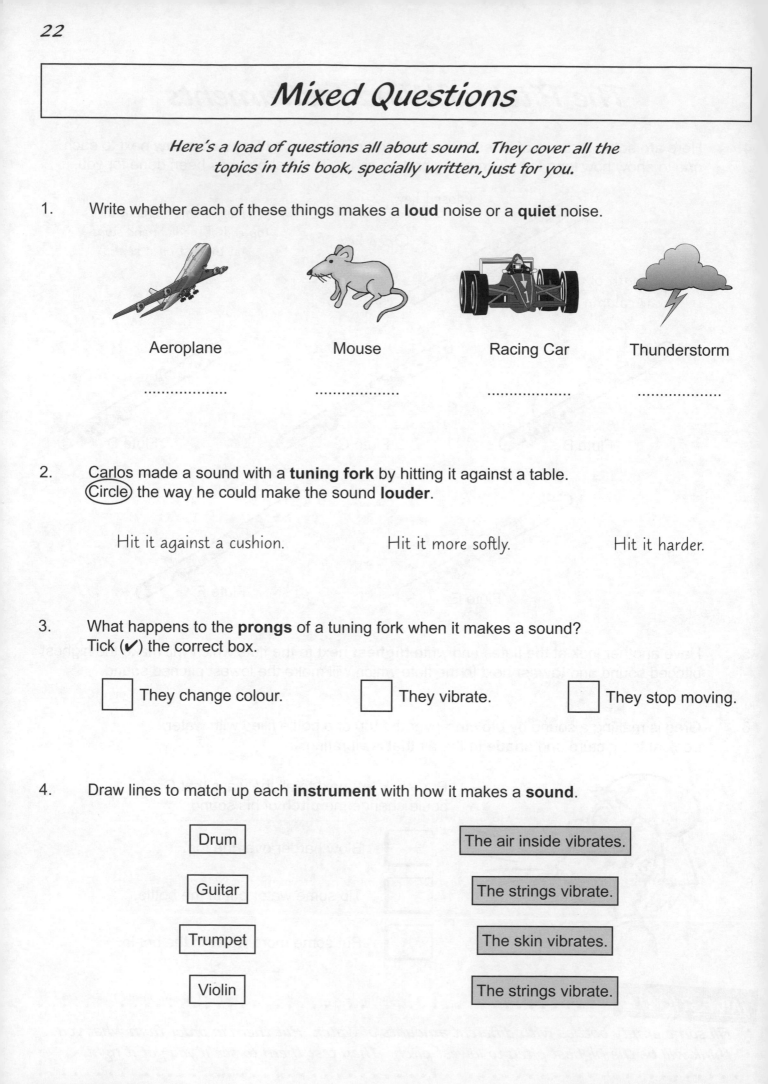

Aeroplane   Mouse   Racing Car   Thunderstorm

....

2. Carlos made a sound with a **tuning fork** by hitting it against a table.
(Circle) the way he could make the sound **louder**.

   Hit it against a cushion.   Hit it more softly.   Hit it harder.

3. What happens to the **prongs** of a tuning fork when it makes a sound?
Tick (✔) the correct box.

   ☐ They change colour.   ☐ They vibrate.   ☐ They stop moving.

4. Draw lines to match up each **instrument** with how it makes a **sound**.

Drum		The air inside vibrates.
Guitar		The strings vibrate.
Trumpet		The skin vibrates.
Violin		The strings vibrate.

Mixed Questions

5. Veronika wants to make her alarm clock **quieter**. (Circle) the **three** things below that would be **best** at **muffling** the sound of the alarm clock.

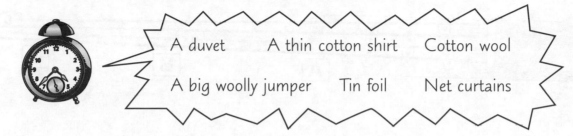

A duvet   A thin cotton shirt   Cotton wool

A big woolly jumper   Tin foil   Net curtains

6. Finish off the sentences by **underlining** the right words in **capitals**.

A big drum makes a LOWER / HIGHER pitched sound than a small drum. Blowing over

a small bottle makes a LOWER / HIGHER pitched sound than blowing over a large

bottle because the column of vibrating AIR / WATER inside is SHORTER / LONGER.

7. Captain Phil is playing his electric guitar very loudly. Write down **three** materials the sound travels through before reaching the shark.

1. ....

2. ....

3. ....

Which part of the shark's body does the
sound have to travel to for the shark to hear it? ....

8. Look at the diagram below. Pete and Dan are playing their guitars in the fields at the **same volume**, but Pete's guitar sounds **louder** to Jen than Dan' guitar.
Which **field** is Pete in? Tick (✔) the correct box.

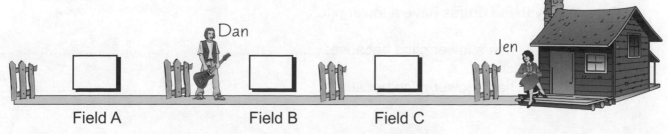

Field A   Field B   Field C

Mixed Questions

Mixed Questions

9.   Look at my **bass guitar** and then answer the questions below.

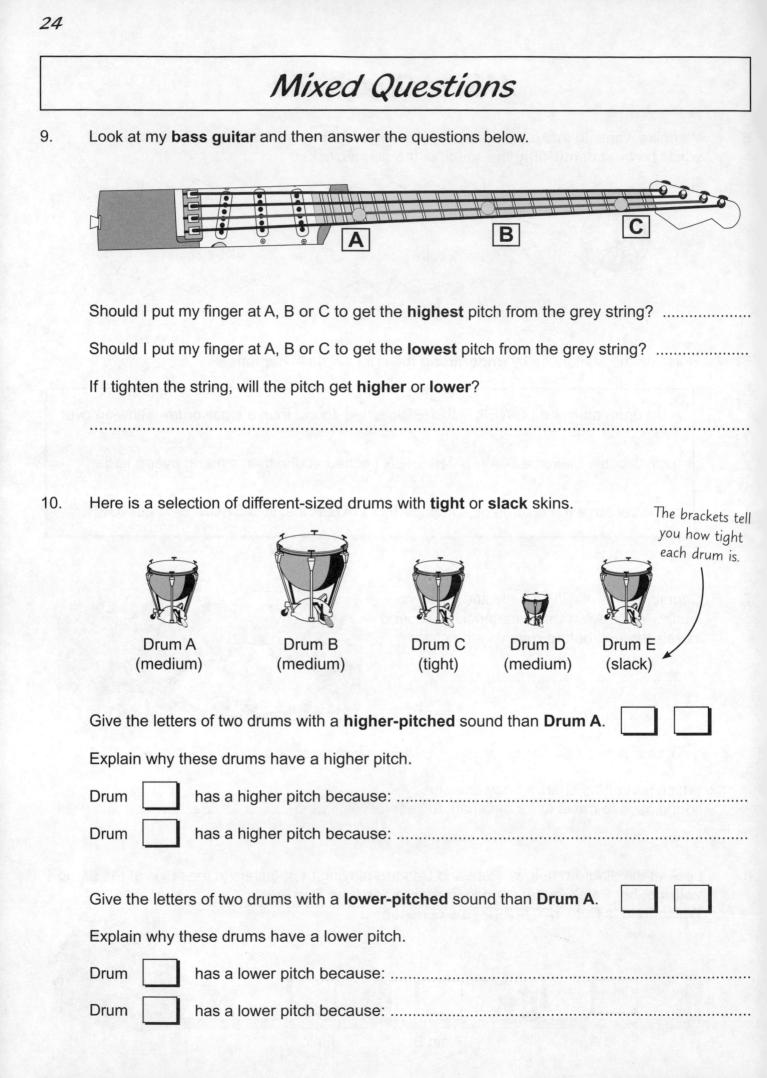

Should I put my finger at A, B or C to get the **highest** pitch from the grey string? ....

Should I put my finger at A, B or C to get the **lowest** pitch from the grey string? ....

If I tighten the string, will the pitch get **higher** or **lower**?

....

10.   Here is a selection of different-sized drums with **tight** or **slack** skins.

The brackets tell you how tight each drum is.

Drum A   Drum B   Drum C   Drum D   Drum E
(medium)   (medium)   (tight)   (medium)   (slack)

Give the letters of two drums with a **higher-pitched** sound than **Drum A**.　□ □

Explain why these drums have a higher pitch.

Drum □ has a higher pitch because: ....

Drum □ has a higher pitch because: ....

Give the letters of two drums with a **lower-pitched** sound than **Drum A**.　□ □

Explain why these drums have a lower pitch.

Drum □ has a lower pitch because: ....

Drum □ has a lower pitch because: ....

Mixed Questions

11.   Gavin is making a sound by **blowing** over the top of a bottle half-filled with water.

What would happen to the volume of the sound
if he blew **harder**? Explain your answer.

..........The sound would be..

..........because the.....................in the bottle..............

..........would be vibrating more...

What would happen to the volume of the sound if he blew more **softly**? Explain your answer.

....

....

What would happen to the pitch of the sound if he added **more water**? Explain your answer.

....

....

What would happen to the pitch if there was **less water** in the bottle? Explain your answer.

....

....

12.   Look at the picture below. If the plumber hits the short pipe Bernard
can't hear it, but if he hits the long pipe Bernard **can** hear it.

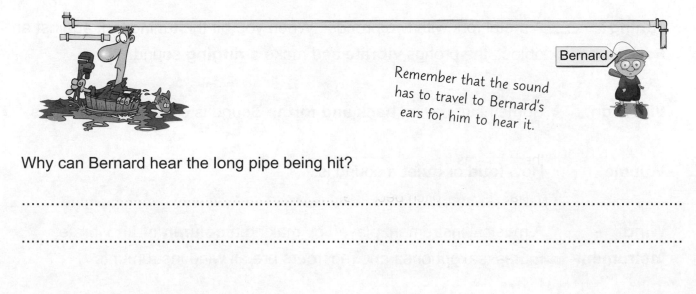

Remember that the sound
has to travel to Bernard's
ears for him to hear it.

Why can Bernard hear the long pipe being hit?

....

....

Mixed Questions

Glossary

Loudness	How **loud** or **quiet** a sound is. Car horns and fireworks are loud. Mice and whispers are quiet.
Muffle	Making a sound **quieter** by stopping vibrations from travelling to the ear. Ear defenders muffle sound.
Musical Instrument	An object that is used to make musical **sounds**.
Note	A sound with a certain **pitch**. Music is made up of different notes.
Pitch	This means how **high** or **low** a sound is.
Pluck	This is how **guitars** are played. Plucking strings makes them vibrate.
Slack	Something that is **loose**. Slack things make **low-pitched** sounds.
Sound	**Vibrations** travelling through a material (such as air).
Stringed Instrument	A musical instrument played by making **strings** vibrate. Guitars, violins and cellos are all stringed instruments.
Tuning Fork	A metal fork with two prongs. When you hit the tuning fork against an object, the prongs **vibrate** and make a **ringing** sound.
Vibration	Something moving **back and forth**. Sound is caused by vibrations.
Volume	How **loud** or **quiet** a sound is.
Wind Instrument	A musical instrument played by making a **column of air** vibrate. Flutes, saxophones and recorders are all wind instruments.

S4D22